AUDITION SONGS

TODAY'S HITS

TEN GREAT SONGS IDEAL FOR AUDITIONS

WISE PUBLICATIONS
PART OF THE MUSIC SALES GROUP
LONDON / NEW YORK / PARIS / SYDNEY / COPENHAGEN / BERLIN / MADRID / TOKYO

Published by
WISE PUBLICATIONS
14-15 Berners Street, London W1T 3LJ, UK.

Exclusive Distributors:
MUSIC SALES LIMITED
Distribution Centre, Newmarket Road,
Bury St Edmunds, Suffolk IP33 3YB, UK.
MUSIC SALES PTY LIMITED
20 Resolution Drive, Caringbah, NSW 2229, Australia.

Order No. AM994884
ISBN 978-1-84772-670-4
This book © Copyright 2008 Wise Publications,
a division of Music Sales Limited.

Compiled by Nick Crispin.
Music edited by Fiona Bolton.
Printed in the EU.

CD recorded, mixed and mastered by Jonas Persson.
Backing tracks arranged by Paul Honey.
Keyboard by Paul Honey.
Guitars by Arthur Dick.
Bass by Don Richardson.
Drums by Chris Baron.

Your Guarantee of Quality:
As publishers, we strive to produce every book
to the highest commercial standards.
The music has been freshly engraved and the book has
been carefully designed to minimise awkward page turns
and to make playing from it a real pleasure.
Particular care has been given to specifying acid-free,
neutral-sized paper made from pulps which have not been
elemental chlorine bleached.
This pulp is from farmed sustainable forests and was
produced with special regard for the environment.
Throughout, the printing and binding have been planned
to ensure a sturdy, attractive publication which should give
years of enjoyment.
If your copy fails to meet our high standards, please
inform us and we will gladly replace it.

www.musicsales.com

CHASING PAVEMENTS

MUSIC BY ADELE ADKINS & FRANCIS WHITE

1. I've made up my mind,— don't need to think it o-ver. If I'm wrong I am— right,— don't need to look no fur-ther. This ain't lust, I_____ know this is love. 2. But if

BLEEDING LOVE

WORDS & MUSIC BY JESSE McCARTNEY & RYAN TEDDER

But noth-ing's great-er than the rush that comes with your em - brace, and in this world of lone-

-li - ness I see your face,__ yet ev - 'ry - one a - round__

__ me thinks that I'm go - ing cra - zy._____ May - be, may - be.

D.S. al Coda

Coda

And it's drain - ing all____ of me._____ Oh, they

find it hard to be-lieve, I'll be wear-ing these scars for ev-

-'ry-one to see. I don't care what they say, I'm in love with you.

They try to pull me a-way, but they don't know the truth. My heart's crip-pled by the

vein that I keep on clos-ing. Ooh, you cut me o-pen and I

HURT

WORDS & MUSIC BY CHRISTINA AGUILERA,
LINDA PERRY & MARK RONSON

1. Seems like it was yes - ter - day when I saw your face.
2. Some days I feel broke in - side, but I won't ad - mit it.

you.

2° play both hands 8ve lower till *

You told me how proud you were, but I walked a - way.
Some - times I just wan - na hide, 'cause it's you I miss.

16

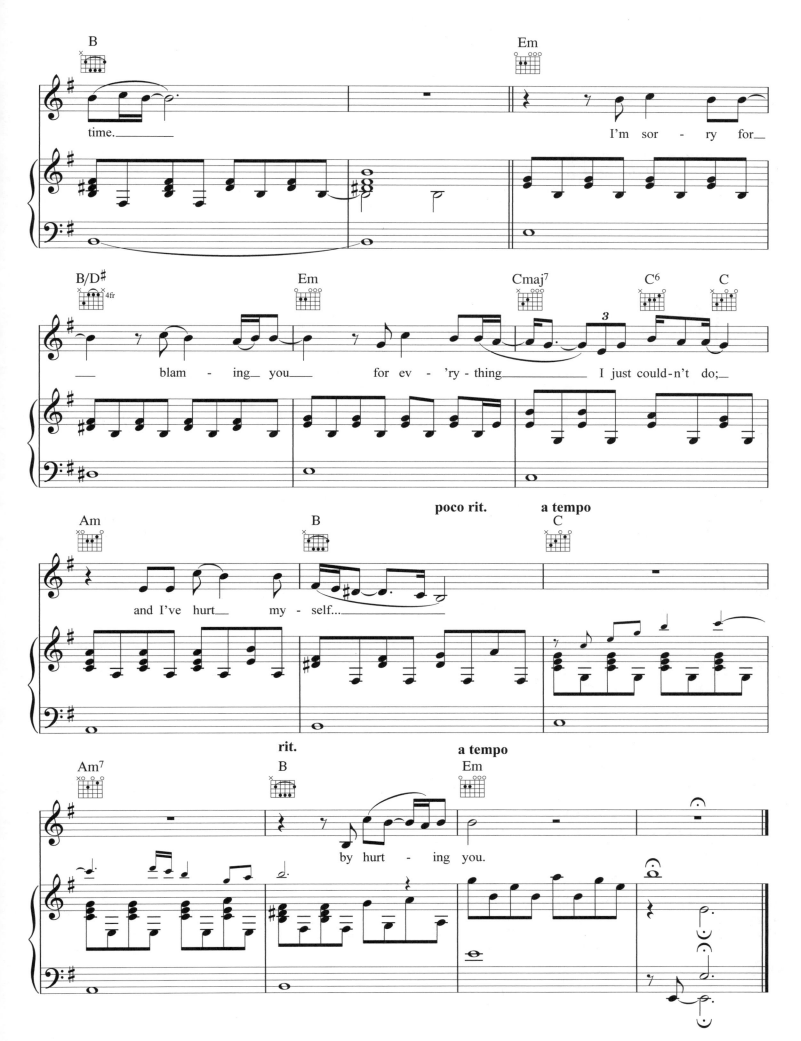

LOVE SONG

WORDS & MUSIC BY SARA BAREILLES

MERCY

WORDS & MUSIC BY DUFFY & STEPHEN BOOKER

31

1234

WORDS & MUSIC BY FEIST & SALLY SELTMANN

1. One, two, three, four, tell me that you love me more. Sleep-less long nights,
2. Sweet-heart, bit-ter-heart, now I can tell you a-part. Co-sy and cold,

that is what my youth was for. Old teen-age hopes are a-live at your door,
put the horse be-fore the cart. Those teen-age hopes who have tears in their eyes,

PUT YOUR RECORDS ON

WORDS & MUSIC BY CORINNE BAILEY RAE, JOHN BECK & STEVEN CHRISANTHOU

SUDDENLY I SEE

WORDS & MUSIC BY KT TUNSTALL

I can see her eyes look-ing from a page in a ma-ga-zine.

She makes_ me feel_ like I could be a tow-er.

Big_ strong tow-er, yeah._ The pow-er to be,_ the pow-er to give, the pow-er to see,_ yeah, yeah._ (Sud-den-ly I

UMBRELLA

WORDS & MUSIC BY CHRISTOPHER STEWART, TERIUS NASH, SHAWN CARTER & THADDIS HARRELL

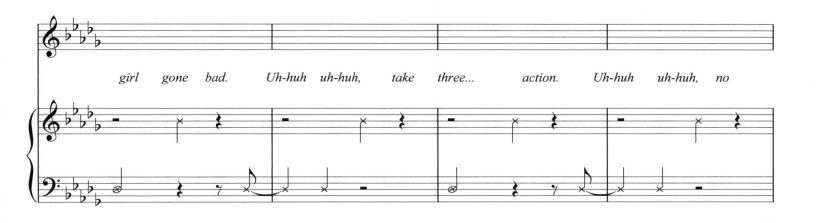

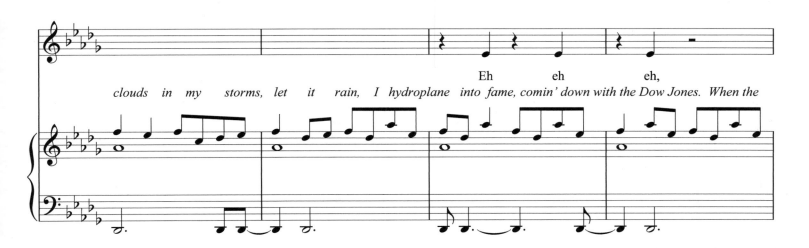

clouds come we gone,   we Rocafella,   she fly higher than weather   and she rocks it better.

eh eh eh   eh.

You know me   an anticipation for precipitation, stacks chips for the rainy day

Eh   eh   eh,   eh eh eh   eh.   1. You
Jay   rain man is back with little Ms. Sunshine Rihanna,   where you at?

G♭maj⁷

D♭/A♭

had my heart,__   and we'll nev-er be worlds a-part,__   may-be in
(2.) fan-cy things,   will nev-er come in-be-tween;   you're part of my

WHEN YOU'RE GONE

WORDS & MUSIC BY AVRIL LAVIGNE & BUTCH WALKER

1. I al-ways need-ed time on my own,
(2.) nev-er felt this way be-fore,

— I nev-er thought I'd need you there when I cry. And the
— ev-'ry-thing that I do re-minds me of you. And the

2. I've

2.

Bm   C   G

We were made for each oth - er,_____ out here for - ev -

-er,_____ I know we were._____ Yeah,_____ yeah._

Bm/F#   B/F#

All I ev-er want-ed was for you to know,_ ev-'ry-thing I do I give my heart and soul,_

I can hard-ly breathe I need to feel you here_ with me,_____ yeah._____ When you're

gone, the piec - es of _ my heart____ are miss-ing you.____ When you're gone,_

61

23456789
1/09(168337)

Make a big impression with these song collections for auditions...

Audition Songs for Female Singers
Piano/vocal/guitar arrangements with CD backing tracks

Don't Cry For Me Argentina...
plus Adelaide's Lament, Big Spender; Heaven Help My Heart; I Cain't Say No; I Will Survive; Out Here On My Own; Saving All My Love For You; Someone To Watch Over Me; The Wind Beneath My Wings. ORDER NO. AM92587

I Dreamed A Dream...
plus Another Suitcase In Another Hall; Fame; If I Were A Bell; Miss Byrd; Save The Best For Last; Someone Else's Story; There Are Worse Things I Could Do; What I Did For Love; You Can Always Count On Me. ORDER NO. AM950224

Memory...
plus Can't Help Lovin' Dat Man; Crazy; Diamonds Are A Girl's Best Friend; Now That I've Seen Her; Show Me Heaven; That Ole Devil Called Love; The Winner Takes It All; Wishing You Were Somehow Here Again; The Reason. ORDER NO. AM955284

I Don't Know How To Love Him...
plus As Long As He Needs Me; Constant Craving; Feeling Good; I Say A Little Prayer; If My Friends Could See Me Now; It's Oh So Quiet; Killing Me Softly With His Song; Tell Me It's Not True; You Must Love Me. ORDER NO. AM955295

Beautiful...
plus Complicated; Don't Know Why; For What It's Worth; I'm Gonna Getcha Good!; Kiss Kiss; No More Drama; One Day I'll Fly Away; A Thousand Miles; Whenever, Wherever. ORDER NO. AM977130

Hits of the 90s
All Mine; Baby One More Time; Black Velvet; Chains; Don't Speak; From A Distance; Hero; Lovefool; Road Rage; What Can I Do. ORDER NO. AM966658

Blues
Cry Me A River; Black Coffee; Fine And Mellow (My Man Don't Love Me); The Lady Sings The Blues; Lover Man (Oh Where Can You Be); God Bless' The Child; Moonglow; Natural Blues; Please Send Me Someone To Love; Solitude. ORDER NO. AM966669

Classic Soul
Don't Make Me Over; I Just Want To Make Love To You; Midnight Train To Georgia; Nutbush City Limits; Private Number; Rescue Me; Respect; Son Of A Preacher Man; Stay With Me Baby; (Take A Little) Piece Of My Heart. ORDER NO. AM966670

R&B Hits
Ain't It Funny; AM To PM; Family Affair; Freak Like Me; Get The Party Started; How Come You Don't Call Me; Shoulda Woulda Coulda; Sweet Baby; Survivor; What About Us? ORDER NO. AM967351

Cabaret Songs
Big Spender; Cabaret; Falling In Love Again; I Am A Vamp; If My Friends Could See Me Now; The Ladies Who Lunch; Maybe This Time; Mein Herr; No Regrets (Non, Je Ne Regrette Rien); Take Me To Your Heart Again (La Vie En Rose). ORDER NO. AM958881

Classical Greats
Caro Mio Ben; Caro Nome; Habanera; Panis Angelicus; The Silver Swan; The Trout; Voi Che Sapete; When I Am Laid In Earth; Widmung; Wohin?. ORDER NO. AM984632

Number One Hits
American Pie; Can't Get You Out Of My Head; Don't Speak; Eternal Flame; Freak Like Me; I Will Always Love You; I Will Survive; Nothing Compares 2 U; The Winner Takes It All; A Woman In Love; plus ten more big songs (2 CDs). ORDER NO. AM91540

Audition Songs For Professional Singers
Black Velvet; Breathless; Emotion; From A Distance; Hero; History Repeating; My Love Is Your Love; Perfect Moment; Search For The Hero; That Don't Impress Me Much; Whole Again; plus 20 more top songs (2 CDs). ORDER NO. AM974578

Pop Hits For Professional Singers
Born To Try; The Closest Thing To Crazy; Don't Know Why; Hopelessly Devoted To You; I'm Gonna Getcha Good!; My Heart Will Go On; Son Of A Preacher Man; plus 20 more big hits (2 CDs). ORDER NO. AM90077

ALL TITLES AVAILABLE FROM GOOD MUSIC RETAILERS OR,
IN CASE OF DIFFICULTY, CONTACT THE MARKETING DEPTARTMENT,
MUSIC SALES LIMITED, NEWMARKET ROAD,
BURY ST EDMUNDS, SUFFOLK IP33 3YB
marketing@musicsales.co.uk

CD TRACK LISTING

CHASING PAVEMENTS
ADELE
CD TRACK 1
(WHITE/ADKINS) UNIVERSAL MUSIC PUBLISHING LIMITED.

BLEEDING LOVE
LEONA LEWIS
CD TRACK 2
(MCCARTNEY/TEDDER) WARNER/CHAPPELL ARTEMIS MUSIC LIMITED/KOBALT MUSIC PUBLISHING LIMITED.

HURT
CHRISTINA AGUILERA
CD TRACK 3
(AGUILERA/PERRY/RONSON)
EMI MUSIC PUBLISHING LIMITED/FAMOUS MUSIC PUBLISHING LIMITED/UNIVERSAL MUSIC PUBLISHING MGB LIMITED.

LOVE SONG
SARA BAREILLES
CD TRACK 4
(BAREILLES) SONY/ATV MUSIC PUBLISHING (UK) LIMITED.

MERCY
DUFFY
CD TRACK 5
(BOOKER/DUFFY) EMI MUSIC PUBLISHING LIMITED/UNIVERSAL MUSIC PUBLISHING LIMITED.

1234
FEIST
CD TRACK 6
(SELTMANN/FEIST) CANDID MUSIC PUBLISHING LIMITED/UNIVERSAL MUSIC PUBLISHING MGB LIMITED.

PUT YOUR RECORDS ON
CORINNE BAILEY RAE
CD TRACK 7
(BECK/CHRISANTHOU/BAILEY RAE) GOOD GROOVE SONGS LIMITED/GLOBAL TALENT PUBLISHING.

SUDDENLY I SEE
KT TUNSTALL
CD TRACK 8
(TUNSTALL) SONY/ATV MUSIC PUBLISHING (UK) LIMITED.

UMBRELLA
RIHANNA
CD TRACK 9
(STEWART/NASH/CARTER/HARRELL) WARNER/CHAPPELL NORTH AMERICA/PEERMUSIC (UK) LIMITED/
EMI MUSIC PUBLISHING LIMITED/SONY/ATV MUSIC PUBLISHING (UK) LIMITED.

WHEN YOU'RE GONE
AVRIL LAVIGNE
CD TRACK 10
(LAVIGNE/WALKER) UNIVERSAL MUSIC PUBLISHING LIMITED/EMI MUSIC PUBLISHING LIMITED.